100 "Tactical Fork" Chess Puzzles for Beginners (Rating 900-1200)

100 real-life chess tactics puzzles for beginners to make you a better player

D1157932

100 "Tactical Fork" Chess Puzzles for Beginners (Rating 900-1200)

Published by **www.chess-books.co.uk**

ISBN: 978-1-78933-329-9

Copyright © 2021 Mr Chess Puzzles

Cover Image Copyright: Shutterstock

Table of Contents

Introduction...4

The Puzzles 7

Get Free Chess Puzzles...59

Introduction

Hi! I'm Mr Chess Puzzles and I'm here to make you a better chess player.

Chess puzzles are an essential part of your development as a player and contribute a massively to your tactical understanding of the game. Even Grandmasters devote time every day to solving chess puzzles to keep them sharp and improve their chess "intuition".

Right from the opening and on into the middle and end game, strong chess players always have an eye out for opportunities to use *tactics* and will quickly recognize positions on the board that are similar to set-ups they have studied in tactical puzzles. Building this intuition quickly helps you spot unexpected *smiting* moves and longer combinations that your opponent hasn't seen. They will save you time on the board by teaching you where to look, and help build the kind of vision that will make your rating skyrocket.

However, a word of caution! While solving chess puzzles will absolutely improve your calculation and strategy skills, you need to also develop a feel for *when* to start calculating in a real game because most games you play will begin with a *quiet* position. For that reason you should concurrently develop your understanding of *positional* chess which breaks down into building strong openings and knowing how to develop your pieces so that they work together on the board. Studying chess tactics is essential but knowing when to start looking for them in an actual game is an important skill too, otherwise you'll just run out your clock.

As a rule of thumb, you should spend more time calculating tactics in a game when there is *tension* on the board. Often (but of course, not exclusively) this is when the opening is complete and opposing pieces are starting to come into contact.

The types of puzzles that will improve your game most quickly are the ones that have been played by real people (every puzzle in this book has been taken from an actual game), and you should steer away from complicated imaginary positions that wouldn't appear in a real life. They can be fun, but you want to focus on plausible chess situations. It's all about building great and relevant chess intuition that you can on the board.

Get Free Chess Puzzles

If you want to get better quickly, you can download our free book of 300 mixed chess puzzles from:

www.chess-books.co.uk/free

or by scanning this QR code with your smart phone

You'll get 300 mixed chess puzzles that start from beginner and move right through to fiendish levels!

All you need to do is fill in the form and we'll email you your book immediately.

Download it now!

The Puzzles

Ready to dive in?

The chess puzzles in this book are all taken from real-life games and are solved by finding a way to win or force a decisive advantage with a "fork" – where one piece simultaneously attacks two opposing pieces.

The solutions are written on the page directly after the puzzles for easy reference, but no peeking!

The best way to train your brain is to try and solve a puzzle in its entirety before looking at any part of the solution.

For best results:

Set up the position on a physical chess board and give yourself 10 minutes to explore the first three strongest looking candidate moves. These include moves that *force* a response from your opponent, such as checks or the potential capture of an undefended piece.

For each move, explore the opponent's possible responses and then calculate what subsequent move would be strongest for you in return. This should lead you towards the solution.

Spend more time exploring the moves that look to give a more positive outcome, but don't forget that the best moves aren't always the most intuitive ones – at least not yet!

If none of your initial moves offer an immediately positive outcome, then look for a positional move that help develop your pieces so you can gain an advantage or make subsequent forcing move.

Remember that forks, skewers, decoys, double attacks, and mating patterns are all things you should be looking out for when learning to solve chess puzzles.

1 - White to Move

2 - White to Move

3 - White to Move

4 - White to Move

Solutions

1)   1. Qxh7+ Kxh7 2. Ng5+ Kg8 3. Nxe6

2)   1. f5+ Kf6 2. fxg6

3)   1. e6+ Ke8 2. exd7+

4)   1. f6+ Kf8 2. fxe7+

5 - White to Move

6 - Black to Move

7 - Black to Move

8 - White to Move

Solutions

5) 1. g3+ Kxh3 2. gxf4+

6) 1... Nxd3 2. Qd2 Nxc1

7) 1... Qc1+ 2. Re1 Qxe1+ 3. Rf1 Qxf1#

8) 1. Nxe6

9 - White to Move

10 - Black to Move

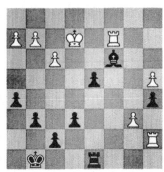

11 - White to Move

12 - White to Move

Solutions

9) 1. e6+ Ke7 2. exd7

10) 1... d3+ 2. Kd1 dxc2+

11) 1. Ne5+ Ke7 2. Nxc6+

12) 1. Qxb8+ Bxb8 2. Rd8+ Qe8 3. Rxe8#

13 - White to Move

14 - White to Move

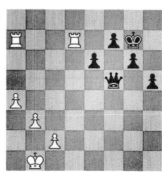

15 - White to Move

16 - White to Move

Solutions

13) 1. Rxd3 Rxd3 2. Nc5+ Kf7 3. Nxd3

14) 1. Rxf7+ Qxf7 2. Rxf7+ Kxf7 3. a5

15) 1. f7+ Qxf7 2. Rxf7

16) 1. Rxa6 Qxa6 2. Nc5+ Kd5 3. Nxa6

17 - Black to Move

18 - White to Move

19 - Black to Move

20 - Black to Move

Solutions

17) 1... Rxc5 2. Rxc5 Bd4+ 3. Kh2 Bxc5

18) 1. Nb6+ Kb8 2. Nd7+ Kc7 3. Nxf8+

19) 1... Kxe7 2. Rxa5 Nc4+ 3. Kd3 Nxa5

20) 1... c5+ 2. Bxc5 dxc5+

21 - White to Move

22 - Black to Move

23 - Black to Move

24 - White to Move

Solutions

21) 1. Rxd8+ Kh7 2. Bd3+ Qxd3 3. Rxd3

22) 1... fxg2+ 2. Kg1 gxf1=Q#

23) 1... d4+ 2. Kd2 dxc3+

24) 1. c6+ Kb8 2. cxd7

25 - White to Move

26 - White to Move

27 - Black to Move

28 - Black to Move

Solutions

25) 1. Bxf5+ Rxf5 2. Rxe8+ Qxe8 3. Qxf5+

26) 1. Rxg7+ Kxg7 2. Bd4+ Kf7 3. Bxa1

27) 1... Qxb4 2. axb4 Nxc2+ 3. Kd2 Nxa1

28) 1... Qg5+ 2. Kf1 Qxf6

29 - White to Move

30 - Black to Move

31 - Black to Move

32 - Black to Move

Solutions

29) 1. d6+ Kh8 2. dxc7

30) 1... Ne6+ 2. Ke5 Nxc7 3. Kd6 Nb5+

31) 1... Nxe3 2. Rxd8 Nxc4 3. Rxa8 Rxa8

32) 1... Bxg2+ 2. Kxg2 Rxe2+ 3. Rxe2 Rxe2+

33 - White to Move

34 - White to Move

35 - Black to Move

36 - White to Move

Solutions

33) 1. Ng6+ Kf5 2. Nxf8 Kg4 3. Ng6

34) 1. Bxf7+ Kh8 2. Bxe8 Qxg2+ 3. Qxg2 Bxg2+ 4. Kxg2

35) 1... Nd7+ 2. Kg7 Nxc5 3. h6 Ne6+

36) 1. Qf8+ Kd7 2. Qxa8

37 - White to Move

38 - White to Move

39 - White to Move

40 - White to Move

Solutions

37) 1. Ne7+ Rxe7 2. Qxd8+ Re8 3. Qxe8#

38) 1. Rxd8+ Bxd8 2. Qe8+ Kh7 3. Qxd8 Qb1+ 4. Kg2

39) 1. Qf6+ Bg7 2. Qxg7#

40) 1. Rf8+ Qxf8 2. exf8=Q#

41 - Black to Move

42 - Black to Move

43 - White to Move

44 - White to Move

Solutions

41) 1... Qxe1+ 2. Qf1 Rxf1#

42) 1... Qxf2+ 2. Kh1 Qf1+ 3. Ng1 Nf2#

43) 1. Bc6+ Kf8 2. Qxc3

44) 1. Nd4 Qe4 2. Nxe2

45 - White to Move

46 - White to Move

47 - White to Move

48 - Black to Move

Solutions

45) 1. gxf3 Rxd7 2. Nf8+ Kg8 3. Nxd7

46) 1. Bxf7+ Kh8 2. Bxe8

47) 1. Rb8+ Rd8 2. Rxd8+ Kh7 3. g6+ fxg6+ 4. fxg6#

48) 1... Nf3+ 2. Kh1 Rg1#

49 - White to Move

50 - Black to Move

51 - White to Move

52 - White to Move

Solutions

49) 1. Nf5+ Kf7 2. Nxe7 Kxe7 3. Rxc7+ Ke6 4. Rxc6+

50) 1... Rf1+ 2. Kh2 Rh1#

51) 1. Qxc8+ Rd8 2. Qxd8#

52) 1. Bxd4 Qxd4 2. Qxc6+ Kf8 3. Qxa8+

53 - Black to Move

54 - White to Move

55 - White to Move

56 - Black to Move

Solutions

53) 1... dxe2 2. Rxd8+ Kf7

54) 1. Qxd8+ Kh7 2. Qxe7 Qb6+ 3. Kf1

55) 1. Qxf7+ Kh8 2. Qxf8#

56) 1... Bxc3+ 2. bxc3 Qxc3+ 3. Nd2 Qxa1

57 - Black to Move

58 - White to Move

59 - Black to Move

60 - Black to Move

Solutions

57) 1... Rxc1 2. Rxc1 Qxd2+ 3. Be2 Qxc1

58) 1. Bxf7+ Kxf7 2. Qf4+ Kg7 3. Qe5+ Kh6 4. Qxc5

59) 1... Qd5+ 2. Qf3 Qxf3+ 3. Rxf3 Rd1+ 4. Rf1 Rxf1#

60) 1... Qc1+ 2. Kg2 Qxb2+ 3. Bf2 Qxa3

61 - Black to Move

62 - Black to Move

63 - White to Move

64 - Black to Move

Solutions

61) 1... d3+ 2. Kd1 dxe2+

62) 1... Nb4+ 2. Ka1 Nc2+ 3. Kb1 Nxe3+

63) 1. Qxc4 Rxd2 2. Qxb3

64) 1... f4+ 2. gxf4+ gxf4+ 3. Kf2 e3+ 4. Ke1 exd2+

65 - White to Move

66 - White to Move

67 - Black to Move

68 - Black to Move

Solutions

65) 1. Rxe8 Rxe8 2. Bxf7+ Kh8 3. Bxe8

66) 1. Qh5+ Bh6 2. Qxh6+ Kg8 3. Qh7#

67) 1... Rxe1+ 2. Kf2 Ng4+ 3. Kxe1 Nxh2

68) 1... Qf2+ 2. Kh1 Qxd2

69 - Black to Move

70 - Black to Move

71 - Black to Move

72 - Black to Move

Solutions

69) 1... Qg4+ 2. Kf1 Rxh1#

70) 1... Qxe4 2. Nxc5 Qxh1

71) 1... Nd3+ 2. Kf3 Nxb4

72) 1... Nd3+ 2. Kd2 Nxe1 3. Kxe1 Rxb1+

73 - Black to Move

74 - White to Move

75 - White to Move

76 - White to Move

Solutions

73) 1... Rxh3+ 2. gxh3 g2+ 3. Bxg2 Qxg2#

74) 1. Ne7+ Kg7 2. Nxc6+

75) 1. Qc8+ Qf8 2. Qxf8+ Rg8 3. hxg8=Q#

76) 1. Ne7+ Kf8 2. Nxd5 Rb1+ 3. Rxb1 Rxb1+ 4. Kh2

77 - Black to Move

78 - Black to Move

79 - Black to Move

80 - White to Move

Solutions

77) 1... d3+ 2. Kd1 dxc2+

78) 1... Qe1+ 2. Qf1 Bxf2+ 3. Kh1 Qxf1#

79) 1... Qxc3+ 2. Bd2 Qxc4

80) 1. Rc8+ Ke7 2. Rxh8

81 - Black to Move

82 - White to Move

83 - Black to Move

84 - White to Move

Solutions

81) 1... Qxc5+ 2. Rf2 Qxe7

82) 1. e5+ Qf5 2. Nh4+ Kg5 3. Nxf5

83) 1... dxe3+ 2. Ke2 exd2

84) 1. Rxg7+ Qxg7 2. Qxe6+

85 - White to Move

86 - White to Move

87 - Black to Move

88 - White to Move

Solutions

85) 1. Rh8+ Qxh8 2. Rxh8+ Kxh8 3. Qh6+ Kg8 4. Qg6+

86) 1. Nxe5 Bxe5 2. Qh5+ Qf7 3. Qxe5

87) 1... Rxf2+ 2. Kxf2 Ng4+ 3. Ke1 Nxh6

88) 1. f6+ Kg8 2. f7+ Kxf7 3. g6+ Kg7 4. gxh7 h3+ 5. Kf2

89 - Black to Move

90 - Black to Move

91 - Black to Move

92 - White to Move

Solutions

89) 1... Be3+ 2. Kh1 Bxc5 3. Qxc5 dxc5

90) 1... Rg2+ 2. Qxg2 hxg2+

91) 1... Nxf3+ 2. Kg2 Nxe1+ 3. Rxe1 Qf3+

92) 1. Nf6+ Kf8 2. Nd7+ Ke8 3. Nxb8

93 - White to Move

94 - Black to Move

95 - White to Move

96 - Black to Move

Solutions

93) 1. fxe6+ Bxe6 2. Rxf6+

94) 1... Nd2+ 2. Ke2 Nxc4+

95) 1. Qd8+ Ka7 2. Qxa5

96) 1... Rxc1 2. Bxc1 Rc8 3. Be3 Rc2+ 4. Kf3 Rxa2

97 - Black to Move

98 - White to Move

99 - White to Move

100 - White to Move

Solutions

97) 1... Bd3+ 2. Kg2 Rxe1 3. Rh8+ Kd7

98) 1. Qe8+ Kh7 2. Qxb5 d2 3. Qxe2 dxe1=R+ 4. Qxe1

99) 1. Nf6+ Qxf6 2. Qh8#

100)   1. Qh6+ Qh7 2. Rf8#

Get Free Chess Puzzles

If you want to get better quickly, you can download our free
book of 300 mixed chess puzzles from:

www.chess-books.co.uk/free

or by scanning this QR code with your smart phone

You'll get 300 mixed chess puzzles that start from beginner and
move right through to fiendish levels!

All you need to do is fill in the form and we'll email you your
book immediately.

Download it now!

Made in the USA
Coppell, TX
03 October 2022

84017986R00036